The Day of Cat

hamlyn

The Day of Cat

Kong Hye Jin

hamlyn

A precious day as recorded by one cat's servant.

Her eyes meet mine as I smooth down the fur on her face and she gazes at me with her light green eyes. When I close my eyes and slowly caress her soft fur, following the soft curve between her head and back, my restless mind calms down from the touch. When I sit daydreaming, then turn my head, she is always there, looking at me, her eyes following me attentively.

I frequently stop what I'm doing – whether laughing, crying, drawing, eating or even sleeping – to look at her. She and I have become friends who naturally exchange glances. Her name is Bono. She is my beloved cat.

I've recorded the moments when I'm being observed by Bono or when I'm observing her. There is a full day of such moments with Bono in this book. While drawing every detail of her body I felt I briefly became my cat. Our relationship developed to the level where I could understand her 'code' and we had a special way of communicating.

Everybody should have his or her own Bono. This book is the result of observing and recording one day in the life of someone precious to me.

I think it's a good idea to look through Bono's whole day as it is shown in this book, a little like caressing her head, and choose a movement that attracts your attention. Then add colours, little by little. At moments throughout the day, depending on what you are doing, find a spot in the illustration that captures your attention and colour in a detail, one at a time. In that way you are paying attention to Bono's day.

Finally, thank you Ms Bono for accepting me as your lowly servant.

If you colour me in with your heart, I will pay you back with my charms.

6:30am

I had a good night's sleep.

I'll have a stretch, then I think I should wake up the servant to make me breakfast.

Hidden pictures

1 butterfly, 2 ostriches

6:50am

Hey servant, wake up!

Why aren't you getting up even when I'm wrapped around your face?

Hidden picture

1 sloth

8:00am

What's this?! How come a grain of steamed rice got stuck here?

Well, since I'm hungry, I'm going to put it in my mouth.

8:30am

After I groom myself like this, nobody can tell me apart from the flowers.

Hidden pictures

2 ostriches, 1 elephant

9:20am

How could I, a nimble hunter, let a fly get away…

Hidden pictures

1 fish, 2 birds

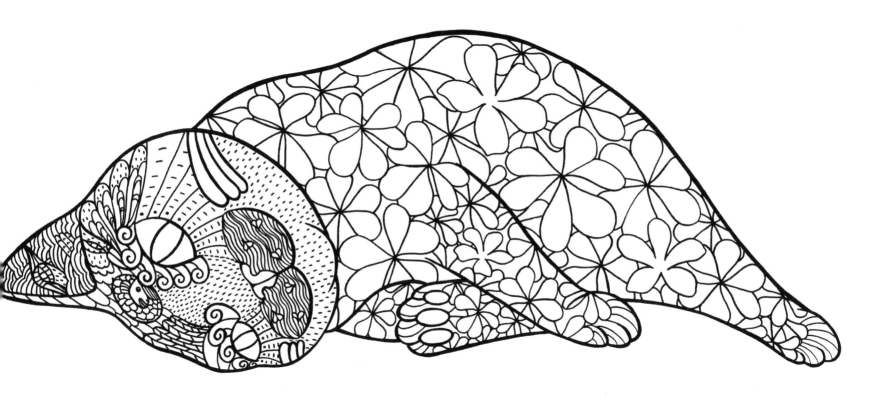

10:30am

A bird is flying away outside the window.

Hidden pictures

1 azalea, 1 bird

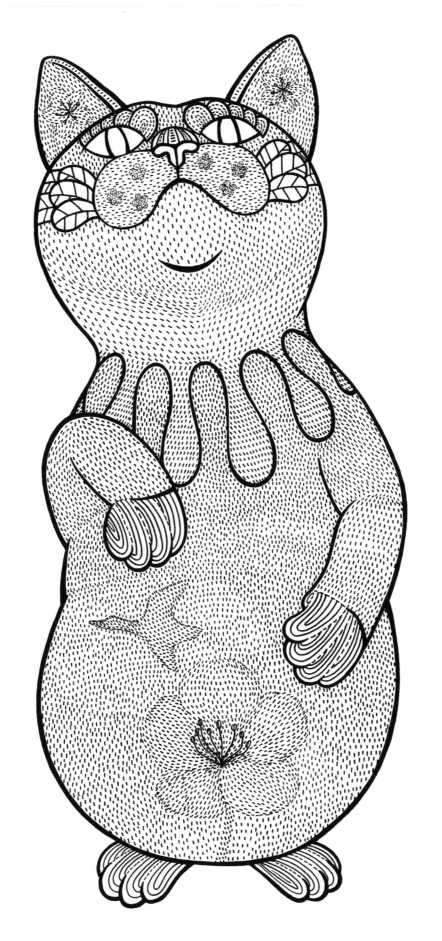

10:50am Try caressing my fur. It will feel like touching flower petals.

11.30am

I'm lying down and looking up at the clouds moving. Ah, that's why people prefer window seats!

Hidden pictures

1 swan, 1 bee

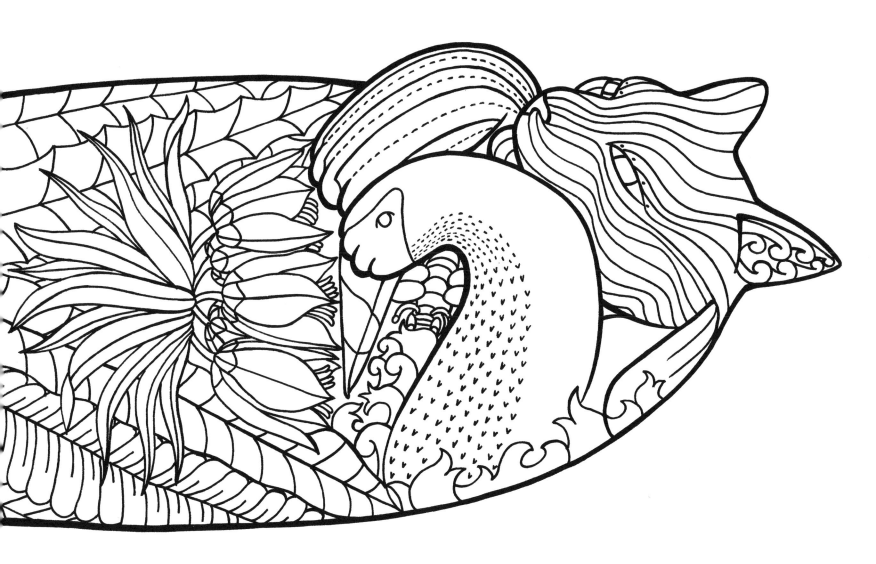

12:10pm

I'm rolling around in the sunlight. It's as wonderful as being in a flower bed.

Hidden picture

1 koala

12:50pm

I shouldn't let my guard down even while taking a nap…I'll arm myself with cuteness.

1:30pm

I need my own time. Please don't interrupt me…meow.

2:00pm

Where are you going? I'm all ready!

Hidden pictures

4 bees

2.20pm

I'm not sleeping.

I'm just closing my eyes

because I'm meditating. Meow.

Hidden pictures
2 owls, 2 fish

2:30pm

My body is perfect. Wherever you look, it's amazing!

Hidden pictures

2 goldfish

3:00pm

A haughty cat posture. Should I try it?

3:30pm

I find myself putting my paws together whenever I imagine something fun to do.

3:50pm

I'm going to win everyone over with my cuteness!

4:00pm

I'm strangely attracted to slippers. What does the servant do with all those slippers?

4:20pm

Each time you bring me something yummy, I'll give you a piece of toilet roll.

Hidden picture

1 peacock

5:00pm

How was your outing, servant?

What's my snack going to be?

Hidden pictures

2 ostriches, 2 caterpillars

5:05pm

If I bow my head too long, it will spoil the servant.

So, I'll count to five and stand up.

Hidden picture

1 owl

5:30pm

Curl your body up as much as possible, so says Bono!

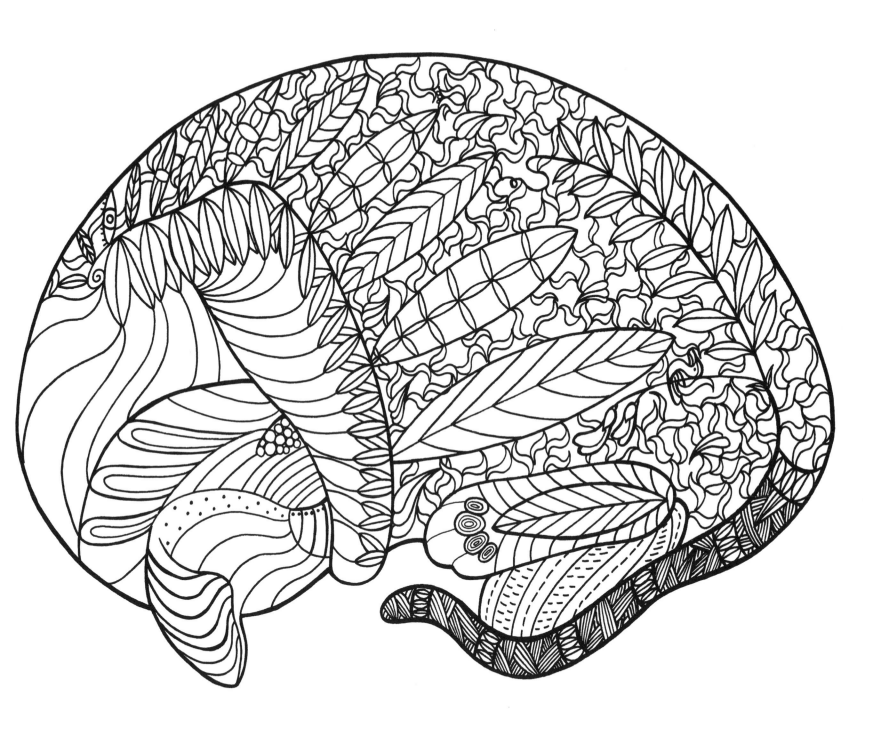

6:00pm

Whenever I see a thread, I automatically turn into a penguin.

Hidden pictures

1 shark, 1 seal, 1 falcon, 1 fish

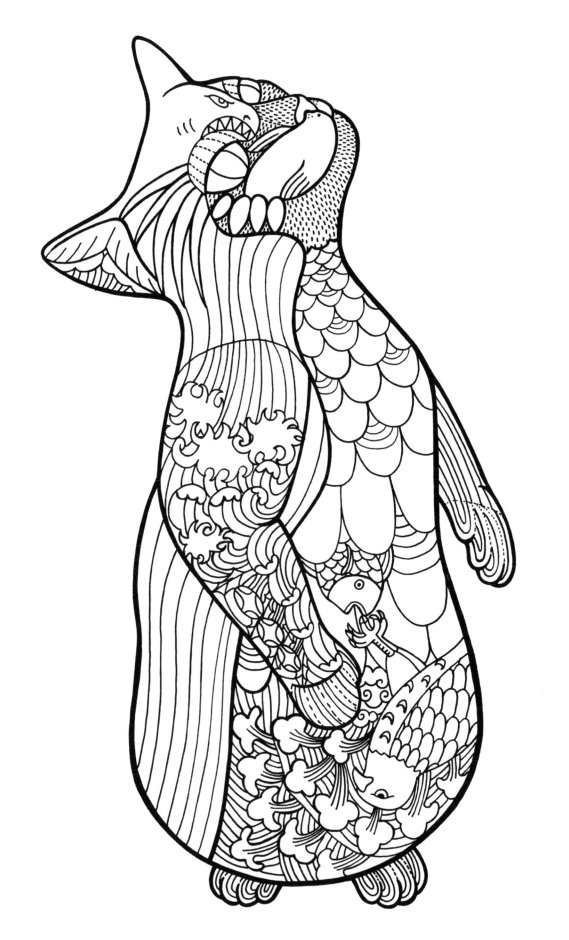

6:30pm

Just wait and see.

As soon as I do this, my servant will run to me right away.

Hidden pictures

1 twisted breadstick, 1 ribbon

6:50pm

I'm having a massage in the servant's lap.

It feels like I'm windsurfing.

Hidden pictures

1 deer, 2 birds

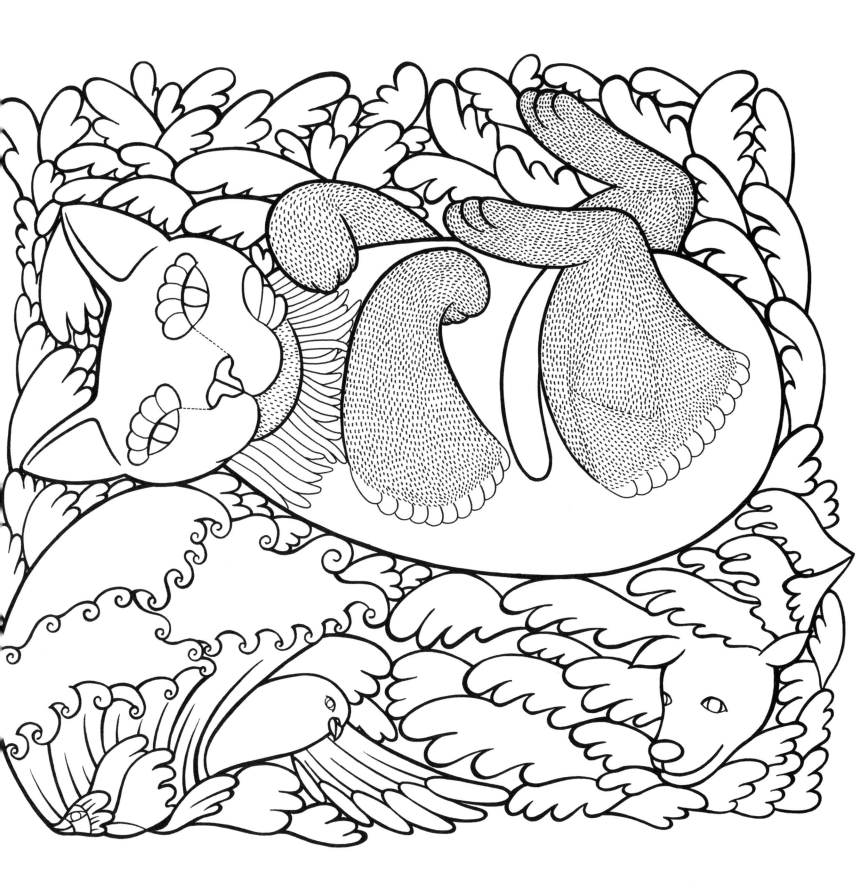

7:00pm

When my picture is being taken, I will make myself out to be the cutest cat in the world.

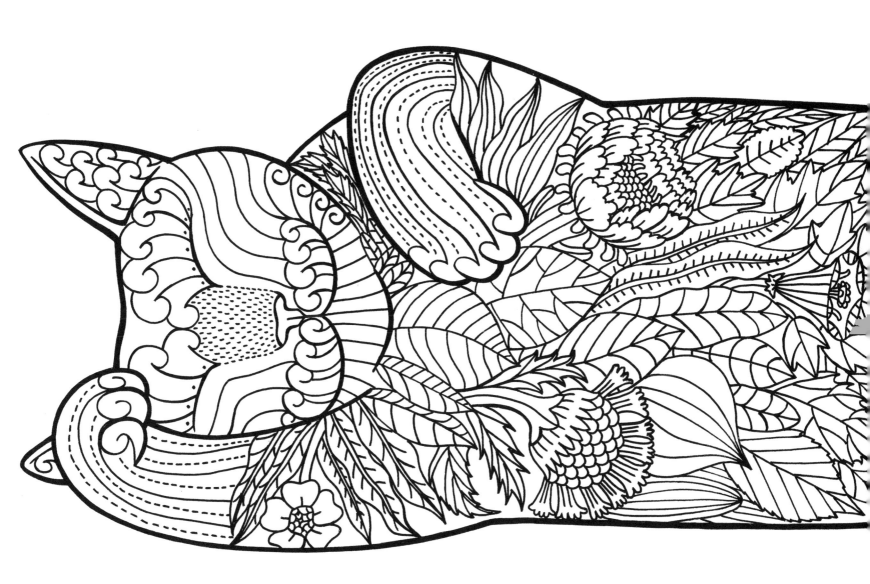

7:20pm

They will think there is a bird in the cat basket.

Hidden pictures

9 birds

7:40pm

I would like to eat with the servant at the table too! Meow.

Hidden pictures

1 rabbit, 1 peacock

7:50pm

As you winked at me once, I'll use the '15 Minute Massage' coupon.

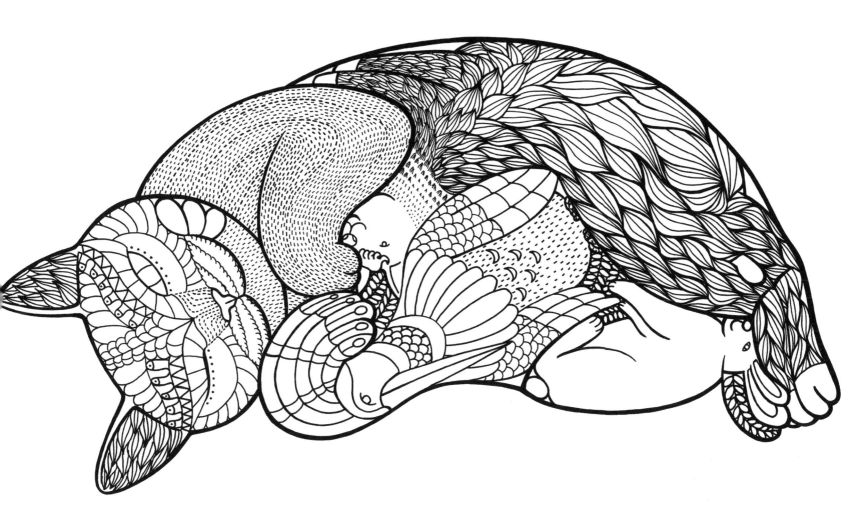

8:00pm

I transformed myself into a glamour puss!

Hidden pictures

1 eagle, 1 mole, 1 seal

8:20pm

When I hug a ball of yarn, I feel like I've been transported to a different world in the blink of an eye.

Hidden pictures

1 ray, 1 shark, 1 octopus, 3 fish

8:40pm

When you look at me sleeping, your mind will become serene.

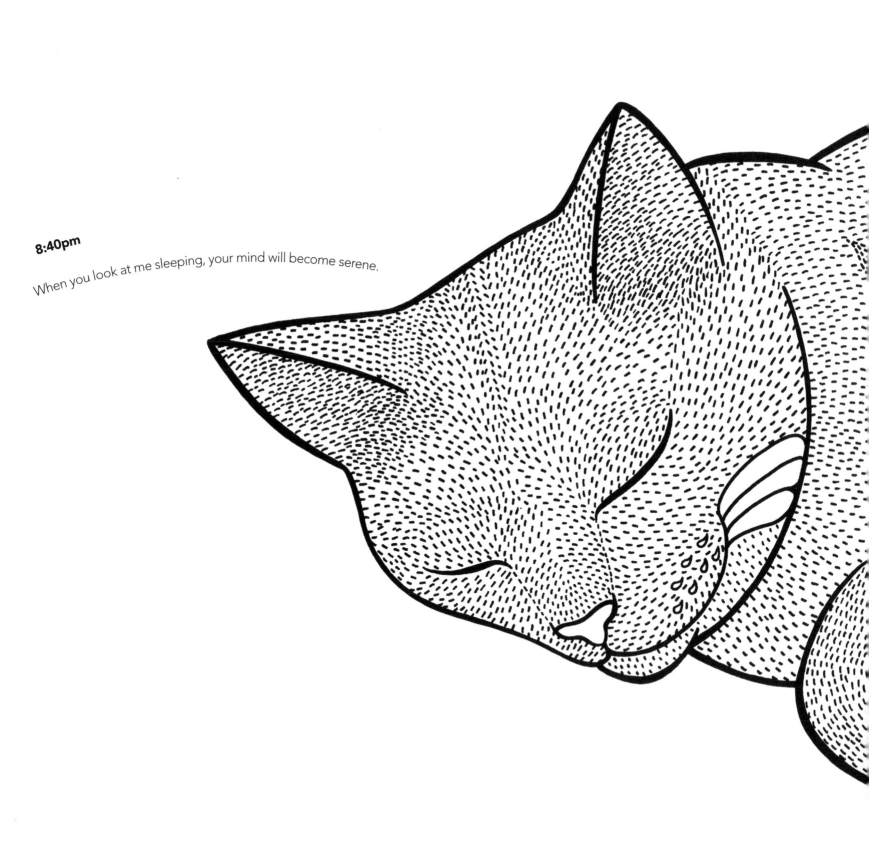

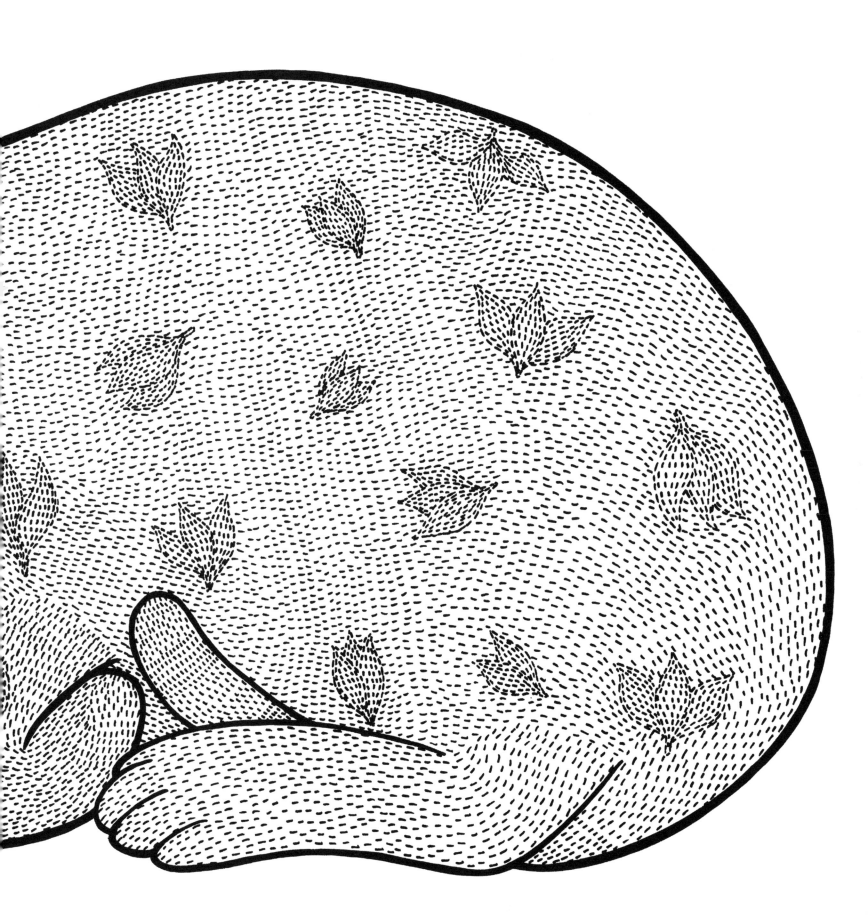

9:00pm

Should I get up?

Or lie down?

Oh! I might stay up all night I'm afraid.

9:20pm

When I receive a massage from the servant, I feel like my body shrinks.

9:40pm

As you gave me such a lovely massage with such devotion I will pay you back with my charms.

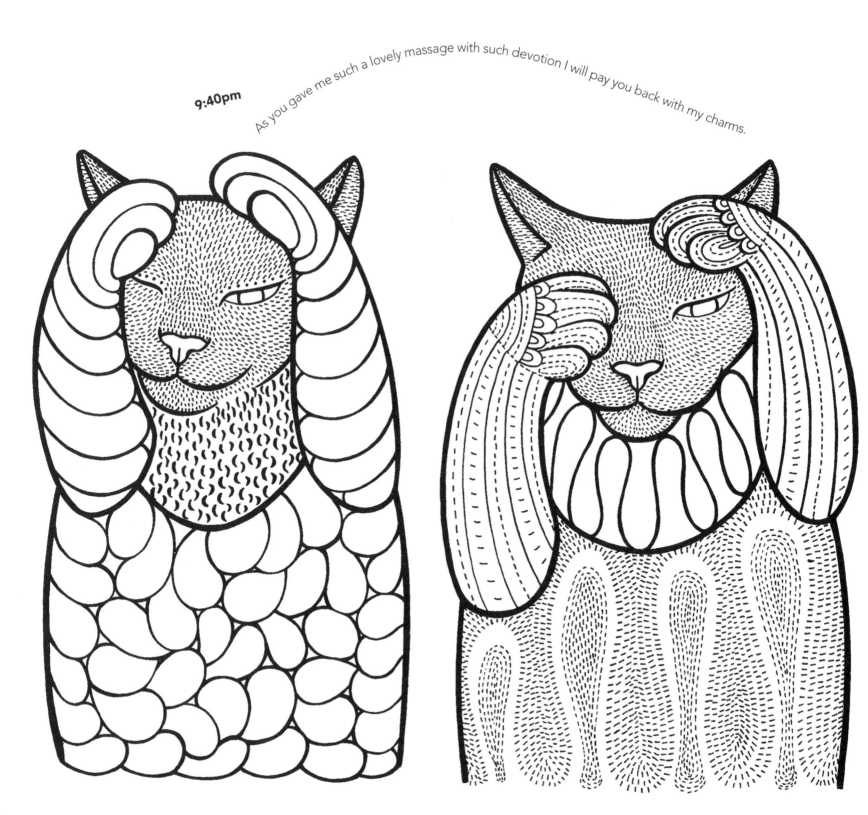

Hidden pictures

1 carp, 1 whale

10:00pm

Stroke me, stroke me, please! Meow.

Hidden pictures

1 bird, 1 ram

10:30pm

When you feel cold and empty, try taking a walk while cuddling me in your arms.

Hidden picture

1 rhinoceros

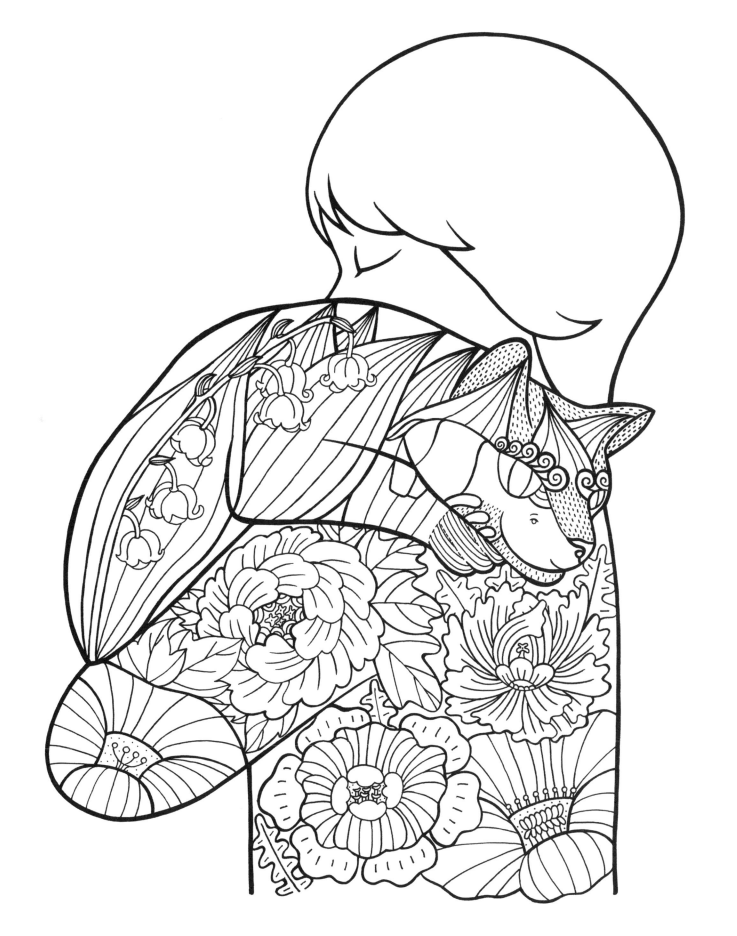

11:00pm

I transform into an owl at night!

Hidden pictures

2 ducks, 1 owl

11:30pm

Since my servant has gone to bed, I'll sleep too.

I'll run around the fields and fly over the ocean in my dreams.

Hidden pictures

1 hawk, 1 octopus, 1 dolphin, 4 fish

12:00am

In my dreams, I keep finding myself in a jungle.

Hidden pictures

2 elephants, 1 meerkat, 1 butterfly, 1 kangaroo, 1 llama

Try writing a letter from the bottom of your heart to someone who is special to you.

Fold along the dotted lines and attach each of the sides using glue to make a pretty envelope for your letter.

Cut along the solid lines. Fold the dotted lines and attach each side with glue.
You will have an octagon-shaped container.

Cut along the solid line and fold the dotted lines to paste the flaps to create a triangular pyramid.

Attach a thread to use it as a mobile for your pet.

Now try drawing a moment you had with someone who is special to you.

The Day of Cat

An Hachette UK Company
www.hachette.co.uk

First published in Korea in 2015 by Munhakdongne Publishing Corporation

This edition published in Great Britain in 2015 by Hamlyn,
a division of Octopus Publishing Group Ltd
Carmelite House, 50 Victoria Embankment, London EC4Y 0DZ
www.octopusbooks.co.uk

ISBN 978-0-600-63376-1

A CIP catalogue record for this book is available from the British Library

Senior Production Manager: Katherine Hockley

Printed and bound in Italy
10 9 8 7 6 5 4 3 2 1